Putting on a Play

THE GREAT FIRE OF LONDON

Written by Tom and Tony Bradman
Illustrated by Andy Catling

WAYLAND

ABOUT THE PLAY

The Great Fire of London is based on the true event of the Great Fire of London, which took place in 1666. However, the characters and story are fictitious. This play can also be used when learning all about the Great Fire of London and what life was like under the Stuarts.

The play be used during Shared or Guided Reading sessions with individuals or small groups of children. It can also be performed by the class with named parts given to individual children and the rest of the class playing the parts of the extras, such as ordinary Londoners, The Watch and the soldiers.

HOW TO STAGE A PLAY

Sets and props

Making the sets and props for the play will be more than half the fun. You'll need to do some research first — what did London and its houses look like in 1666? Once you know what you want to show in your scenes, you could tape together some white paper to make some large backdrops for the play that you then paint to create the sets; you will need a backdrop for the streets of London, Westminster Palace and Pepys's study.

You can perform the play without having to find lots of different props. All you need are some buckets and some barrels of gunpowder, which you can make from cardboard. You can make some cheese from modelling clay for Pepys's Parmesan and use sheets of paper from your classroom for the documents Will finds in Pepys's study.

Staging

There is no need to put on a huge production. All you need is a space where you can put on the play. With a small group you could use part of the classroom, such as your reading area. Or you could move the furniture back and use the whole room. If the whole class is involved, a hall or even the school field will give you all the space you need.

Costumes

Costumes can be simple and you can be as creative as you like with your ideas for each character. What did people wear in 1666? The fire starts at night, so Will and his family will be in nightclothes! The king and Pepys could wear beards made from string and cotton wool, shorts, long socks and shoes with a buckle made from paper stuck to the top. Some children could dress in red, yellow and orange and pretend to be the fire, dancing around on one side of the stage while other children pretend to throw buckets of water at the fire!

HAVE FUN PUTTING ON YOUR PLAY!

Go to www.waylandbooks.co.uk for more ideas.

3

Introduction

This play is set in London in 1666. London is the biggest city in England. The streets are narrow and most of the houses are built of wood. Some even have thatched roofs and have been built very close together, as there are a lot of people living in the city. Too many houses all built so close together is bound to lead to trouble one day...

The characters in the play

- Will Farriner
- Mother
- Father
- Peg
  Will's sister
- King Charles II
- Samuel Pepys
- Elizabeth Pepys
- Captain Wharton
- A Palace Guard
- Narrator
- Extras: Londoners, soldiers and The Watch

SCENE 1

CHARACTERS IN THIS SCENE:

● **Narrator** ● **Will** ● **Mother** ● **Father** ● **Peg**
● **Captain Wharton** ● **Extras – A crowd of people**
and **The Watch**

The stage is divided in half. On one side is **Mr Farriner**'s *bakery, on the other side is the street.*

● **Narrator:** It's just after midnight on the 2nd of September, 1666. Young Will Farriner is asleep in his room, above his family's bakery on Pudding Lane.

● **Will:** *(opening his eyes and sniffing)* Smoke? Oh no! *(He jumps up and runs into his parents' room.)* Quick, everybody... *(shouts)* FIRE!

● **Mother:** *(dozily)* Er... what's going on?

● **Father:** Wake up! The house is on fire!

● **Mother:** *(shouts)* WHAT!? Did you forget to douse the ovens?

Father: Er… Um… There's no time for blame now. We must get out!

Will: I'll wake Peg! *(He shakes **Peg** awake.)* Get up now, Peg! Quickly!

Peg: *(sleepily)* But why? It's the middle of the night!

Will: *(pulling her out of bed)* Don't argue, Peg! Hurry, or we'll be burnt to a crisp!

● **Peg:** Let go of me! *(Pulling her arm out of* **Will***'s grip.)* I'm not leaving without Dolly!

● **Narrator:** Peg finds her favourite doll and the Farriners run outside into the street.

A **crowd** of neighbours has gathered.

● **Will:** The whole house is going up now. I think we'd better move back!

● **Peg:** Does this mean we'll have to buy a new house, Father?

● **Father:** What with? All my money is tied up in that shop! We're ruined!

● **Mother:** At least we're alive, Tom!

● **Narrator:** Just then, Captain Dick Wharton of The Watch arrives with a few men. The Watch is 17th-century London's combined police and fire brigade.

● **Captain Wharton:** Stand clear, everyone! We'll deal with this.

Will: But how? You'll never put out the fire now.

Captain Wharton: But we can stop it spreading by pulling down the other houses. If only we had a few barrels of gunpowder...

The crowd: You can't blow up the houses! They're our homes! Stop!

Captain Wharton: It's too late anyway! Look, another roof is on fire...

SCENE 2

CHARACTERS IN THIS SCENE:

● Narrator ● Will ● Mother ● Father ● Peg
● Captain Wharton   ● Extras – A crowd of people
and The Watch

Will *and his family are watching as* **Captain Wharton** *and* **The Watch** *fight the fire by throwing buckets of water at it. A* **crowd** *gathers.*

● **Narrator:** By the time the sun rises on the 3rd of September, the fire has spread a long way...

● **Will:** Well, that's Pudding Lane gone and the three streets beyond it!

● **Mother:** Hush, Will! You'll worry your father. He's upset enough as it is.

● **Father:** *(moaning)* It's all my fault... I should have made sure the ovens were out. The king will probably hang me...

● **Peg:** It'll be all right, Father.

● **Captain Wharton:** *(yelling)* Hurry, men! Throw some water on that roof over there...

● **Will:** We can help, Captain. What do you want us to do?

● **Captain Wharton:** Good lad! Grab a bucket and join the line!

● **Will:** Mother, Father, you must take Peg to safety!

Mother, **Father** *and* **Peg** *exit, running off stage.*

SCENE 2
CONTINUED

● **Narrator:** With no fire engines, the only way to fight the fire is to throw water at it. People have to pass buckets in a long line from the River Thames...

● **Will:** It's no good, Captain! The fire is spreading even further!

● **Captain Wharton:** There's a strong wind from the east that's making it worse. If only we had gunpowder – then we could blow up the houses and stop the fire spreading! *(suddenly shouts)* Watch out!

Everyone scatters as a nearby roof falls in, smoke and flames billowing.

● **Will:** So, what can we do?

● **Captain Wharton:** Somebody must tell the king what's happening. We need his help.

● **Will:** Leave it to me, Captain. I'll go!

● **Captain Wharton:** *(calling out after him)*
And tell him we need more men...

Will *runs off through the smoke and flames...*

SCENE 3

CHARACTERS IN THIS SCENE:

- Narrator
- Will
- Palace Guard
- Samuel Pepys
- The king
- Extras – courtiers at the royal court

*This scene takes place inside the **king**'s grand chamber at Westminster Palace. There is a **palace guard** at the door and **courtiers** in the room, but the peace is shattered when **Will** bursts in, followed by **Samuel Pepys.***

● **Palace Guard:** Halt! State your business!

● **Will:** I must see the king about the fire!

● **Palace Guard:** Fire? What fire?

● **Will:** The one in the East End. Can't you smell the smoke?

● **Palace Guard:** No, I can't. Be off with you. The king has no time for brats who tell tales!

● **Narrator:** Suddenly Samuel Pepys arrives. He is an important adviser to the king.

*Enter **Samuel Pepys** in a rush.*

● **Pepys:** Let him in, you fool! It's not a lie. I've seen the fire myself.

● **Palace Guard:** *(stammering)* Of course, whatever you say, Mr Pepys!

*The **palace guard** steps away from the door of the **king**'s grand chamber. **Pepys** bursts through the door, followed by **Will**.*

● **Pepys:** My Lord, I have terrible news!

● **Courtiers:** News? What news?

● **The king:** Ah, Pepys, was it you making all that noise? You look a mess.

● **Pepys:** There's a huge fire in the East End.

● **The king:** There's always a fire somewhere in London, my man. That's what The Watch is for.

● **Pepys:** Sire, The Watch needs your help. There may not be a London at all if you don't act soon.

● **The king:** Calm down, Pepys. Who is this young man?

● **Will:** *(stepping forward and bowing)* Will Farriner, Sire, son of Thomas. I've come to ask for your help.

● **The king:** Have you now? Farriner, hmm? I know that name from somewhere.

Will: My father makes pastries for you but the fire destroyed our bakery!

The king: He makes exceedingly good cakes… Very well, Pepys. I shall send for the Army.

SCENE 4

CHARACTERS IN THIS SCENE:

- **Narrator** - **Will** - **The king** - **Captain Wharton**
- **Samuel Pepys** - **Extras – A crowd of people and The Watch**

The Watch *and a* **crowd** *of Londoners are running around in the street, trying to fight the fire. The* **king** *and* **Captain Wharton** *shout orders.*

● **Narrator:** Will, Pepys, the king and a detachment of soldiers arrive at the edge of the fire. Captain Wharton is in charge of the Londoners fighting the blaze.

● **The king:** *(pointing to some* **soldiers***)* You men, help those people. We need buckets, now!

● **Captain Wharton:** It's good to have you here, Your Majesty! The Watch just isn't big enough for this!

● **The king:** Don't worry, Captain Wharton! I'll make sure everyone in London fights the flames if I have to. We must all work together!

● **Captain Wharton:** If only we had some gunpowder! We could blow up these houses and stop the fire spreading.

● **Narrator:** Everyone joins in fighting the fire. People stand in long lines, passing along buckets of water. But the fire keeps spreading…

● **Will:** We'd better help, too, Mr Pepys.

*Pause while everyone tries to put out the fire. After a while, **Samuel Pepys** speaks.*

● **Pepys:** It's no good, London is doomed!

● **Will:** Then I must find my family, Mr Pepys.

● **Pepys:** It's too dangerous – the city is in chaos! You'll have to come with me.

SCENE 5

CHARACTERS IN THIS SCENE:
- **Narrator** • **Will** • **Samuel Pepys**
- **Elizabeth Pepys**

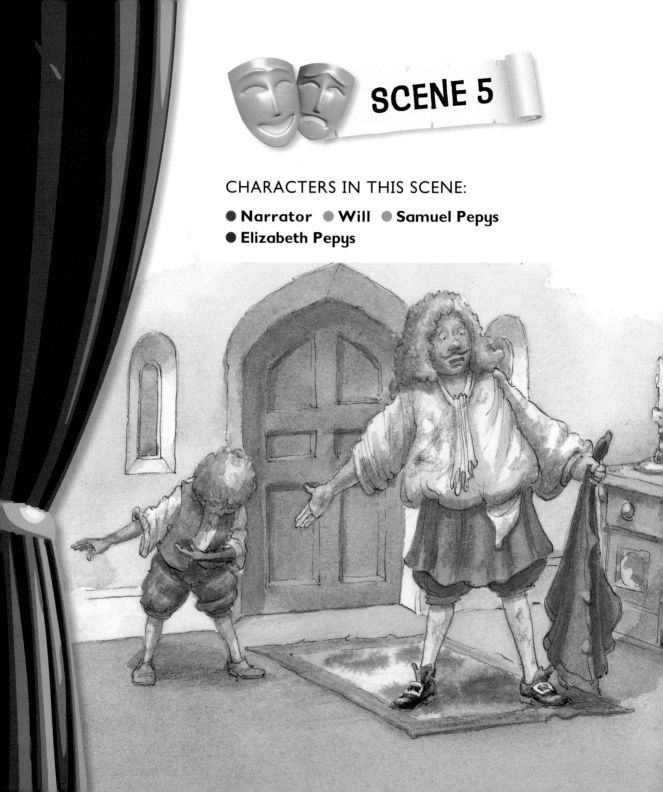

This scene takes place in **Samuel Pepys's** *house. His wife,* **Elizabeth**, *is pacing anxiously.*

● **Narrator:** Pepys takes Will to his home to keep the boy safe and to save his most valuable possessions.

● **Elizabeth:** Samuel! *(rushing to greet* **Pepys** *and* **Will**) Where have you been? I've been so worried!

● **Pepys:** I've been fighting the fire, dear. This is Will, he's been helping, too.

● **Will:** *(bowing)* Pleased to meet you, Mrs Pepys.

● **Elizabeth:** Oh, dear! You both look so tired and such a mess!

Pepys: Elizabeth, can you bring the cheese from the kitchen?

Elizabeth: Cheese? You look like you need a real supper, not just cheese!

Pepys: I'm burying it, my dear, not eating it. To keep it safe from the fire.

Will: You're going to bury your cheese? Are you feeling all right, Mr Pepys?

Pepys: It's a huge piece of Parmesan, Will, worth a lot of money. I'd better bury my official papers, too. Give me a hand here, boy...

Will and **Pepys** *pick up a large box, but it slips and falls to the floor. A lot of papers come flying out.*

Pepys: Oh no! They're all out of order now!

Will: Mr Pepys, *(reading one of the papers)* this says there's lots of gunpowder in the Tower of London. Captain Wharton said he needed gunpowder earlier.

● **Pepys:** Will, you're a genius! Let's go…

● **Elizabeth:** *(stammering)* But you only just got home!

SCENE 6

CHARACTERS IN THIS SCENE:

● Narrator ● Will ● Mother ● Father ● Peg
● The king ● Captain Wharton ● Samuel Pepys
● Extras – A crowd of people, soldiers and The Watch

As **Will** and **Pepys** arrive back, the **king** and **Captain Wharton** are still fighting the fire.

● **Will:** Captain Wharton! Captain Wharton! We know what to do!

● **Captain Wharton:** Calm down, lad. What's going on?

● **Pepys:** Will has an idea. You'd better get the king over, too.

The **king** enters.

● **Will:** There's loads of gunpowder in the Tower, Sir. We can use it to blow up the houses and stop the fire spreading. Just like you said!

● **Crowd:** Stop the fire! Save our houses!

● **The king:** Excellent idea, boy. *(pointing to some soldiers)* You, men, go to the Tower at once!

Soldiers *run to the tower, exiting the stage. Meanwhile* **The Watch** *are still fighting the flames.*

● **Narrator:** The soldiers soon return with barrels of gunpowder.

Enter the **soldiers***.*

● **The king:** Right, everyone get back! Captain, get the powder into those houses.

● **Captain Wharton:** Right you are.

● **The king:** This was your idea, Will. You should light the fuse.

Will *lights the fuse and everyone runs for cover.*
The gunpowder explodes with a huge BANG and a whole
street of houses collapses. Everyone cheers!

● **Captain Wharton:** It worked! The fire's stopped spreading!

● **The king:** You've saved London, lad. Name your reward, anything!

Suddenly **Will***'s family burst through the crowd. They run*
straight to **Will***, not noticing the* **king** *standing close by.*

● **Mother:** Will! Will! Is that you? Are you all right?

● **Will:** I'm fine. Mr Pepys has been looking after me.

● **Father:** *(shaking Pepys's hand)* Thank you, Sir. We've lost everything! We were fearful that we had lost Will, too.

● **Pepys:** Think nothing of it. Will's a hero now!

● **The king:** *(clearing his throat)* Excuse me...

Mother and **Father** see the **king**. **Father** kneels and raises his hands.

● **Father:** I'm so sorry, Your Majesty! I didn't mean to start the fire! It was an accident!

● **The king:** *(shouting)* You did what?

● **Father:** Oh, dear... Well, I...

● **The king:** *(calling to **Captain Wharton**)* Captain Wharton, arrest this man immediately.

● **Will:** Wait! You said I could have a reward!

● **The king:** Make it quick, boy.

● **Will:** I want you to let my father go and give him enough money to start a new bakery.

● **Captain Wharton:** *(under his breath)* I admire the lad's cheek!

The king: Hmmm... Those were exceedingly good cakes... Very well. But Mr Farriner?

Father: Er, yes, my lord?

The king: Do be careful in the future.

Will: Oh, don't worry, Sire. *(smiling)* He will be...

The End

GLOSSARY

detachment
a group
of soldiers

douse
to put
something out

fuse
material along
which a flame
moves

gunpowder
a type of
explosive

The Watch
London's
combined
police and fire
brigade in the
17th century

First published in 2011 by Wayland

Copyright © Wayland 2011

Wayland
338 Euston Road
London
NW1 3BH

Wayland Australia
Level 17/207 Kent Street
Sydney NSW 2000

All rights reserved.

Editor: Katie Woolley
Designer: Elaine Wilkinson
Illustrator: Andy Catling

British Library Cataloguing in
Publication Data

Bradman, Tom.
  The Great Fire of London. –
(Putting on a play)
  1. Great Fire, London, England,
1666–Juvenile drama.
  I. Title II. Series III. Bradman, Tony.
  822.9'2-dc22

ISBN: 978 0 7502 6548 5

Printed in China

Wayland is a division of
Hachette Children's Books,
an Hachette UK company.
www.hachette.co.uk